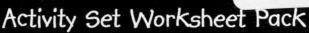

Activity Set Worksheet Pack

Welcome to WriteShop Primary, where your child's creative writing journey begins! This Activity Set Worksheet Pack contains two parts: worksheet pages and evaluation charts.

Activity Set Worksheets

Each lesson in WriteShop Primary Book C has a corresponding worksheet in this Activity Set Worksheet Pack. The workbook pages are designed to introduce important concepts or skills at the beginning of each new writing lesson.

The worksheets are meant to be simple. This simplicity allows your child to practice basic writing concepts, either with your guidance or on his own, without feeling overwhelmed or tense about completing the exercise. If a page seems a bit easy for your child, just let him have fun with it. Remember that the more ways your child can feel successful in the writing environment, the more confidence he will gain as a writer.

The back of many pages of the Activity Set Worksheets provides space for your child to write freely at the level with which he is comfortable. Encourage him and praise him for his efforts. Your attitude is key to modeling enthusiasm and motivation for building creative writing skills. Together, you can find joy in the journey as your child's writing skills develop and grow stronger on the road to successful learning.

Evaluation Charts

The Activity Set Worksheet Pack also contains two Primary Writing Skills Evaluation Charts. Each chart tracks the progress of five lessons. Remove the corresponding chart from the packet at the beginning of Lessons 1 and 6 (or print out each chart if you have the digital version). Keep progress charts in a notebook or file.

The Primary Writing Skills Evaluation Chart is not designed to be used as a grading tool; rather, it's an excellent way to record your child's growth and gain a better grasp of his strengths and weaknesses. In upcoming lessons, you can then focus on specific skills that need improvement.

Published by WriteShop® Inc.
5753 Klusman Avenue, Alta Loma, CA 91737-2223
www.writeshop.com

WriteShop books and products are available at www.writeshop.com or by
contacting WriteShop at (909) 989-5576.

ISBN: 978-1-935027-05-8

Printed in the United States of America

Illustrator: Deborah Thomson
graphics.figgiephotography.com

Mini Story Detective File

Name: _____

Write down ideas for a new mystery.
Cut out each box.
Staple the pages together into a book.

TOP SECRET

TOP SECRET	Title	Character
	_____ _____	_____ _____
Setting	Problem	Solution
_____ _____	_____ _____	_____ _____
Beginning	Middle	End
_____ _____	_____ _____	_____ _____

Make-Believe Journal

Name: _____

Fill in the blanks of your make-believe journal.

My Day As a Bee

Yesterday, I was in my garden when I turned into a

bee! First, I flew to a _____.

(name of a flower)

Then, I landed on a _____.

(name of a plant)

Next, a _____ chased me to

(name of an animal)

_____.

(name of a store)

So I bought a _____.

(name of a thing)

Finally, I turned back into myself. What a day!

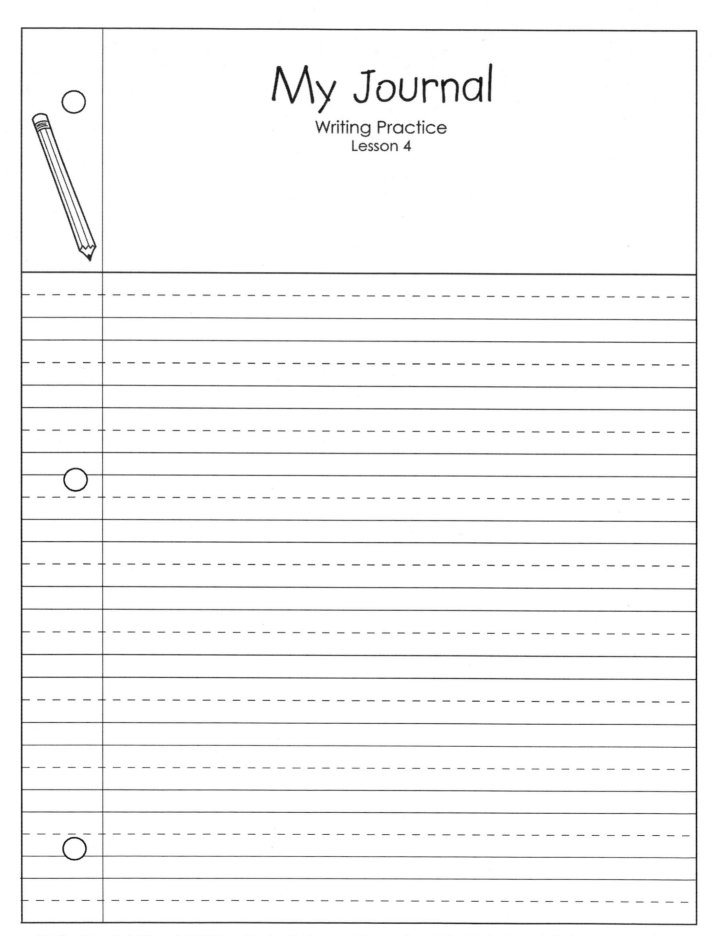

My Journal

Writing Practice
Lesson 4

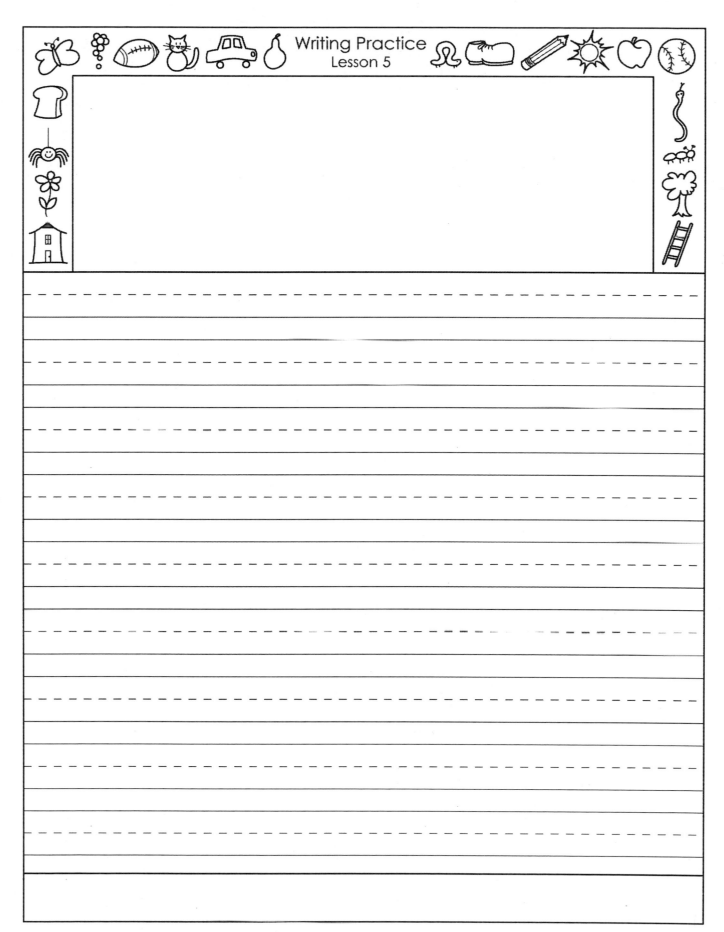

Writing Practice
Lesson 5

Describe the Clown

Name: _____

Directions:

The words in the balloons help describe the clown. Add more describing words to the blank balloons.

Choose which words you want to use. Then write one or two sentences on the blank lines to describe the clown.

silly

big

funny

smiling

red

_____

_____

_____

_____

_____

_____

_____

Writing Practice
Lesson 6

At the Pond

Name: _____

Read the words.
Choose which words you want to use.
Then write one or two sentences on the blank
lines to describe the pond.

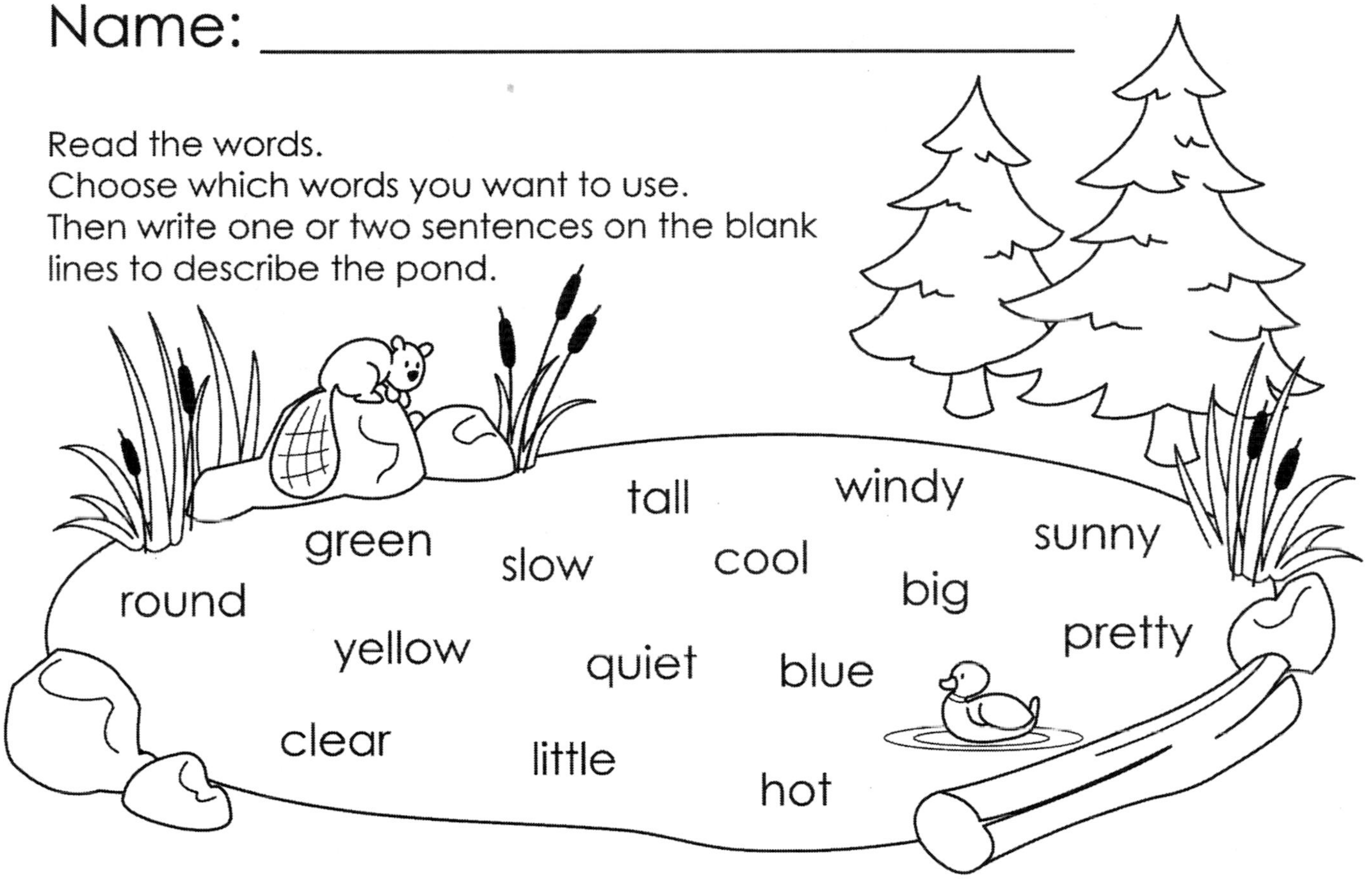

green   tall   windy   sunny
round   slow   cool   big
yellow   quiet   blue   pretty
clear   little   hot

_____

_____

_____

_____

_____

_____

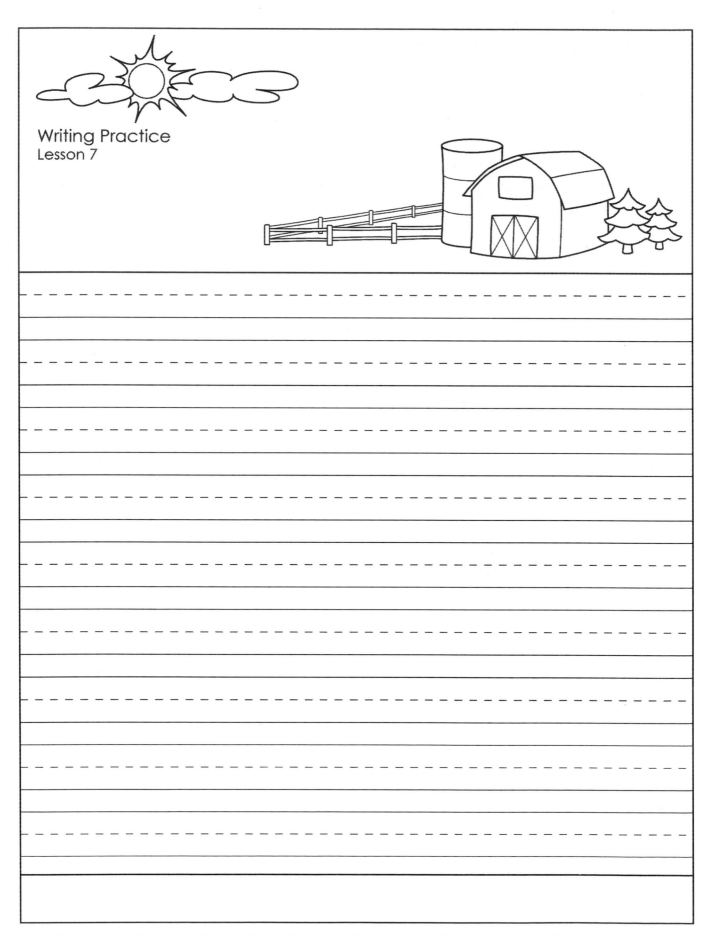

Writing Practice
Lesson 7

Books are Fun!

Name: _____

1. Read the book report.

> This book is about a turtle named Troy. He swam to a deserted island and found a treasure chest, but it was locked and he could not find the key. Troy tried to break the chest open. First he jumped up and down on it. Then he dropped big coconuts on it. Finally, Troy decided to push the chest into the ocean, but it sank to the bottom. The water rusted the lock, so at last Troy could open the chest. It was filled with gold! Troy became the richest turtle in the Seven Seas. I would recommend this book for anyone who likes adventure stories.

2. Circle the best title for this book.
   a. The Golden Coconuts
   b. The Turtle and the Treasure Chest
   c. The Rusted Lock

3. Write the title on the book and draw a picture for the cover.

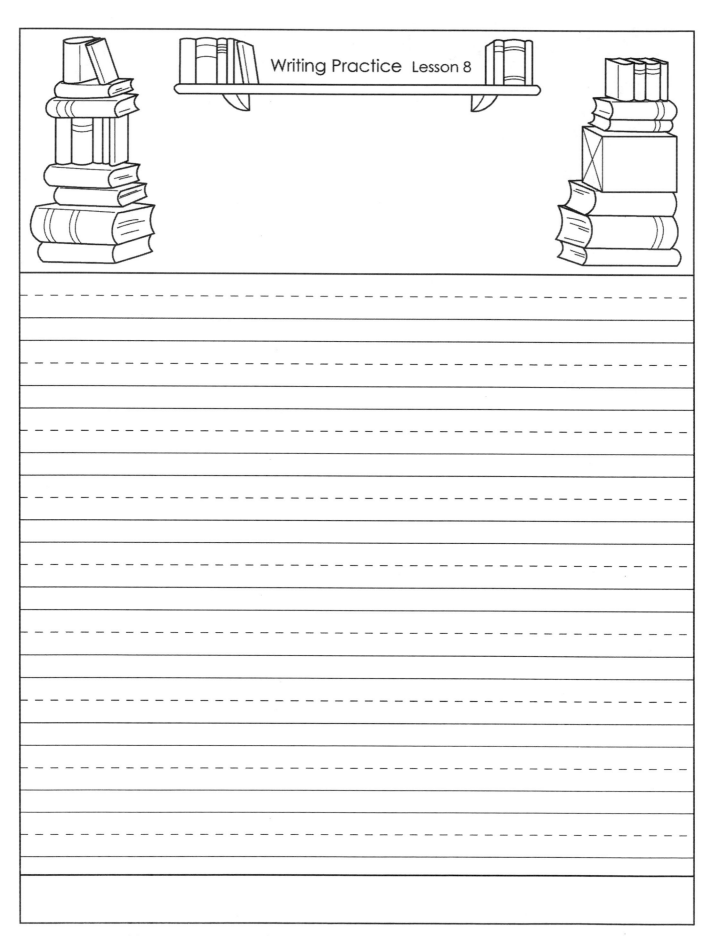

Writing Practice Lesson 8

Find the Facts

Name: _____

Match each picture to the fact that tells about it.
Draw lines to connect the answers.

	It swims in a pond.
	It helps people see in the dark.
	It makes honey.
	It eats honey.
	It gives light to ships in a storm.
	It flies at night.

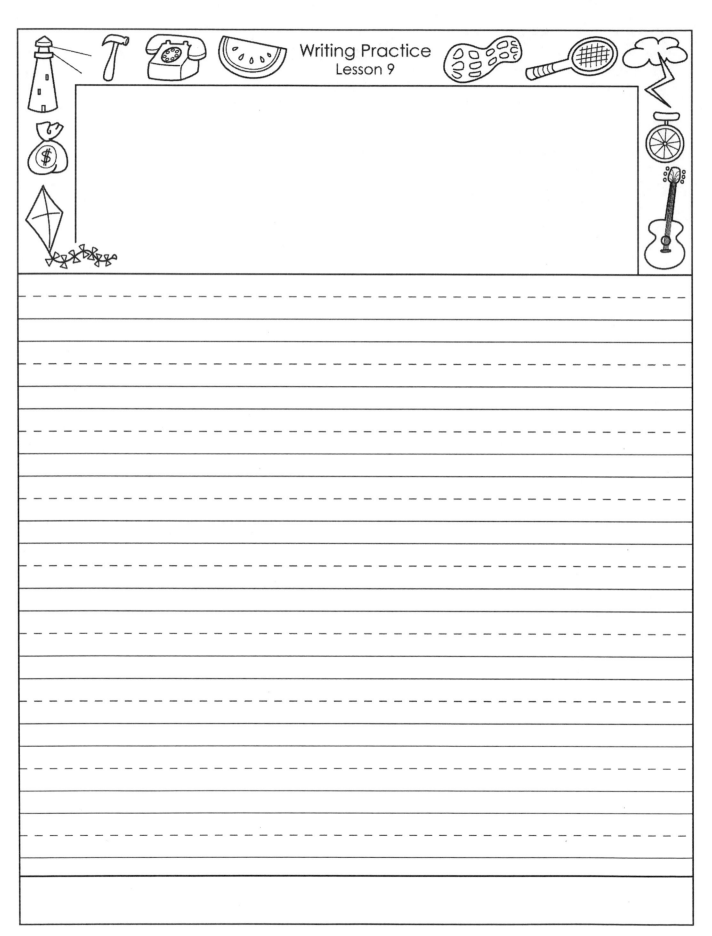

Writing Practice
Lesson 9

Fascinating Facts

Name: _____

Read the facts on this page.
Choose one to write about in a short report.
On the blank lines below, make a list of 3-5 facts you know about the subject.
On the back of the worksheet, write a short report about it. Be sure to
include an introduction, a body, and a closing.

The blue whale is the biggest animal of them all.

 The Nile is the longest river of all.

Thomas Edison invented the light bulb.

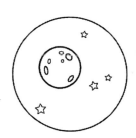 Neil Armstrong was the first person to walk on the moon.

Hawaii is an island in the Pacific Ocean.

_____

_____

_____

_____

_____

Writing Practice Lesson 10

Lessons 1–5   Primary Writing Skills Evaluation Chart

Name: _____

	Lesson 1 Date: ___	Lesson 2 Date: ___	Lesson 3 Date: ___	Lesson 4 Date: ___	Lesson 5 Date: ___
Content					
Uses story organizer to brainstorm and add story details					
Title supports main idea					
Writing Project story makes sense					
Story has beginning, middle, and end					
Story has problem and solution					----
Story has character and setting					----
Writing Skills – *Key steps in the progression of learning to write*					
Writes groups of words					
Writes complete sentences					
Mechanics					
Puts spaces between words					
Puts spaces between sentences					
Uses punctuation at the end of a sentence					
Begins new sentences with capital letters					
Uses quotation marks correctly					
Spells frequently used words correctly					
Uses dictionary or *Super Speller!* to check spelling					
Self-Editing					
Identifies words spelled correctly					
Identifies sentences written correctly					
Identifies some mistakes					
Writes some corrections without help					

Lessons 6-10   Primary Writing Skills Evaluation Chart

Name: _____

	Lesson 6 Date: ____	Lesson 7 Date: ____	Lesson 8 Date: ____	Lesson 9 Date: ____	Lesson 10 Date: ____
Uses graphic organizer to brainstorm and add details to a non-fiction article or report					
Title supports main idea					
Writing Project article or report makes sense					
Article or report has introduction, body, and closing					
Uses adjectives/describing words					
Writing Skills – *Key steps in the progression of learning to write*					
Writes groups of words					
Writes complete sentences					
Mechanics					
Puts spaces between words					
Puts spaces between sentences					
Uses punctuation at the end of a sentence					
Begins new sentences with capital letters					
Uses quotation marks correctly					
Spells frequently used words correctly					
Uses dictionary or *Super Speller!* to check spelling					
Self-Editing					
Identifies words spelled correctly					
Identifies sentences written correctly					
Identifies some mistakes					
Writes some corrections without help					